# FRANKENSTEIN

**A** GRAPHIC CLASSIC BY
**TERRY M. WEST**

**BASED ON THE NOVEL BY**
**MARY SHELLEY**

## SCHOLASTIC INC.

New York   Toronto   London   Auckland   Sydney
Mexico City   New Delhi   Hong Kong

**PENCILLER**
**JAMAL IGLE**

**INKER**
**PHYLLIS NOVIN**

**COLORIST**
**KURT MARQUART**

**LETTERER**
**FRED VAN LENTE**

**COVER ARTIST**
**MICHAEL LILLY**

**COVER COLORS**
**J. BROWN AND TECH FX**

Copyright © 1999 by Scholastic Inc.
All rights reserved. Published by Scholastic Inc.
Printed in the U.S.A. 113

ISBN  0-439-05709-4

28 27 26   R   11 12 13 14/0

# FRANKENSTEIN

**M**ARY SHELLEY AND HER HUSBAND WERE SPENDING THE WEEKEND AT A FRIEND'S HOUSE IN THE COUNTRY. THE YEAR WAS 1817. THERE WAS NO VCR, NO TV, AND NO RADIO. TO KEEP EACH OTHER ENTERTAINED, THEY TOOK TURNS MAKING UP SCARY STORIES.

MARY'S HUSBAND AND THEIR FRIEND WERE FAMOUS WRITERS. BUT IT WAS MARY'S STORY THAT SENT SHIVERS DOWN EVERYONE'S SPINES. IT WAS A TALE ABOUT A SCIENTIST NAMED DR. FRANKENSTEIN, WHO CREATED A HORRIBLE MONSTER THAT HE COULD NOT CONTROL.

THE STORY WAS SO GOOD THAT MARY SHELLEY WROTE IT DOWN AND PUBLISHED IT. <u>FRANKENSTEIN</u> BECAME ONE OF THE MOST FAMOUS MONSTER TALES EVER TOLD.

FOR YEARS, VICTOR FRANKENSTEIN HAS CHASED THIS CREATURE. FIRST THE HUNT TOOK HIM ALL OVER EUROPE. NOW VICTOR HAS SEEN EVERY CORNER OF THE WORLD. THE NORTH POLE WILL BE THE END. VICTOR HAS NEVER BEEN THIS CLOSE TO CATCHING THE CREATURE. HE KNOWS THAT HE DOES NOT HAVE MUCH TIME LEFT. HE IS DYING.

IF HE DOES NOT STOP THE CREATURE NOW, THE NIGHTMARE WILL CONTINUE. BUT HOW DID IT BEGIN? HE THINKS BACK. IT ALL STARTED WITH THE DEATH OF HIS MOTHER ...

④

VICTOR LOVES COLLEGE. HE ESPECIALLY LIKES HIS SCIENCE CLASSES. HE IS EAGER TO LEARN AS MUCH AS HE CAN.

HE LEARNS ANATOMY— THE STUDY OF THE BODY ...

CHEMISTRY— THE STUDY OF SUBSTANCES AND HOW THEY REACT TO EACH OTHER ...

AND PHILOSOPHY— THE STUDY OF IDEAS.

BUT SOON, VICTOR LEARNS EVERYTHING THE PROFESSORS KNOW. HE DECIDES TO SET UP HIS OWN LAB IN HIS APARTMENT.

HE STARTS TO DO HIS OWN SECRET RESEARCH.

VICTOR LOOKS FOR A SECRET NO ONE KNOWS ...

... THE SECRET OF LIFE ITSELF!

I ... I ... I have failed!

VICTOR HAS WORKED TOO HARD. HE IS BECOMING ILL.

I must rest. I will deal with my failure tomorrow.

VICTOR FALLS ASLEEP IMMEDIATELY. HIS SICK BODY IS COVERED WITH SWEAT.

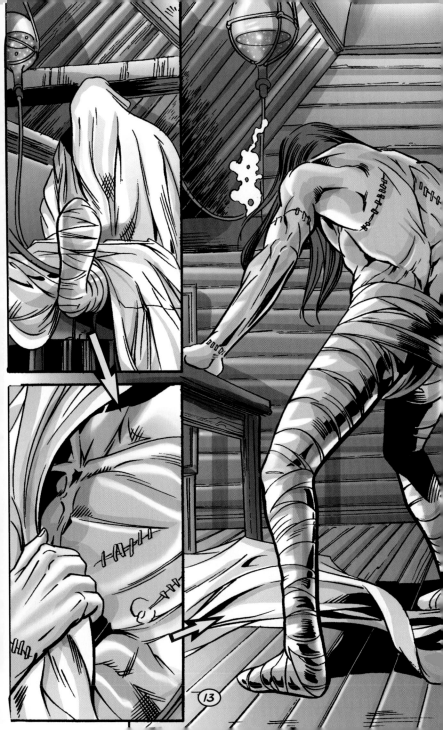

Away, foul creature!! Stay back!

You disgust me! Go back to where you came from!!

THE CREATURE RUNS AWAY IN A PANIC. IT DISAPPEARS INTO THE NIGHT. VICTOR THEN FALLS INTO A DEEP SLEEP. THE SHOCK HAS MADE HIM EVEN SICKER.

A FEW DAYS LATER, VICTOR WAKES UP IN HIS ROOM AT CASTLE FRANKENSTEIN.

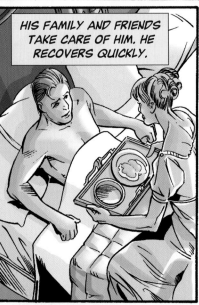

HIS FAMILY AND FRIENDS TAKE CARE OF HIM. HE RECOVERS QUICKLY.

THEY OFTEN ASK HIM ABOUT THE NIGHT HE BECAME ILL.

What happened, my friend?

Nothing that I can speak of.

VICTOR DOESN'T TELL ANYONE ABOUT HIS SECRET RESEARCH. HE CONVINCES HIMSELF THAT THE CREATURE DIED THAT NIGHT.

VICTOR DECIDES NOT TO RETURN TO COLLEGE. HE SETTLES INTO A NORMAL LIFE.

VICTOR DECIDES TO MARRY ELIZABETH AND BEGIN A FAMILY.

Elizabeth, will you marry me?

Yes, my love! I have waited so long to hear those words from you!

I am getting older, my son. You will take over my business after your wedding. You will be master of Castle Frankenstein!

IT IS THE HAPPIEST TIME OF VICTOR'S LIFE. HIS HORRIBLE EXPERIMENT IS NOW JUST A MEMORY.

"THE PEOPLE I SAW THAT NIGHT REACTED IN THE SAME WAY YOU DID. THEY WERE AFRAID AND DISGUSTED."

"I LOOKED FOR SHELTER AWAY FROM THOSE EYES ... SO FULL OF FEAR ... AND HATRED."

"I DID NOT ASK YOU TO MAKE ME, BUT DEEP DOWN, I WANTED TO SURVIVE."

"I TRAVELED FOR DAYS UNTIL I CAME UPON A VILLAGE."

"EVEN THOUGH I'D HAD BAD EXPERIENCES WITH HUMANS, I NEEDED COMPANY. SO I DECIDED TO WATCH THE PEOPLE IN THE VILLAGE."

"I LEARNED MUCH FROM MY NEIGHBORS, AND WATCHING THEM HELPED FILL THE EMPTINESS I FELT INSIDE."

"AT FIRST I WAS CONTENT TO LIVE NEAR THEM. BUT SOON, THESE PEOPLE BECAME LIKE A FAMILY TO ME. I WANTED TO TALK WITH THEM."

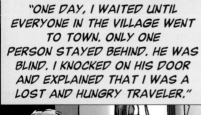

"ONE DAY, I WAITED UNTIL EVERYONE IN THE VILLAGE WENT TO TOWN. ONLY ONE PERSON STAYED BEHIND. HE WAS BLIND. I KNOCKED ON HIS DOOR AND EXPLAINED THAT I WAS A LOST AND HUNGRY TRAVELER."

Come in, my friend. I have soup and bread. I would be happy to share it with you.

"HE HAD A KIND VOICE. HE SPOKE OF NOTHING IMPORTANT, BUT I COULD HAVE LISTENED TO HIM FOREVER. FOR ONCE, I WAS WITH A FRIEND. IT FILLED ME WITH THE MOST JOY I HAD EVER KNOWN."

"UNFORTUNATELY, I SAT WITH HIM TOO LONG."

"THE PEOPLE RETURNED. THEY SAID THAT I WAS NOT FIT FOR THEIR COMPANY. THEN I DECIDED TO FIND YOU. WHY, FRANKENSTEIN? WHY DO PEOPLE FEAR AND HATE ME?"

VICTOR RETURNS TO HIS LAB. HE BEGINS CREATING A BRIDE FOR HIS CREATURE. HE DOES NOT TELL ANYONE WHAT HE IS DOING.

What if the second one is more evil than the first?

VICTOR IS ALMOST FINISHED. THEN HE REALIZES HE CANNOT GO ON.

VICTOR DESTROYS THE LAB AND RETURNS HOME. HE IS TERRIFIED THAT THE CREATURE WILL PUNISH HIM.

TIME PASSES, AND THE CREATURE NEVER RETURNS. VICTOR PREPARES FOR HIS WEDDING.

AFTER THE WEDDING, VICTOR AND ELIZABETH HAVE A WONDERFUL PARTY AT CASTLE FRANKENSTEIN. EVERYONE IS ENJOYING THEMSELVES SO MUCH THAT THEY DON'T WANT TO LEAVE. BUT ELIZABETH IS TIRED AND LEAVES VICTOR TO STAY AND ENTERTAIN THEIR GUESTS.

LATER, VICTOR GOES UPSTAIRS TO SEE ELIZABETH. HE DISCOVERS THAT THE CREATURE HAS KEPT ITS PROMISE.

Elizabeth? *NOOOOOO!!!!*

WHEN THE POLICE ARRIVE, THEY SEARCH THE GROUNDS. THEY FIND THAT VICTOR'S FRIEND HENRY HAS ALSO BEEN KILLED.

I will track you down and destroy you, monster!

A FEW WEEKS LATER, VICTOR'S FATHER DIES OF GRIEF.

I will go to every corner of this earth to find you!

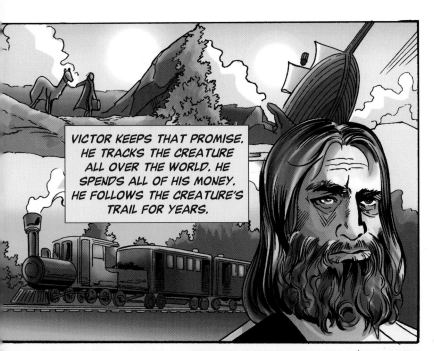

VICTOR KEEPS THAT PROMISE. HE TRACKS THE CREATURE ALL OVER THE WORLD. HE SPENDS ALL OF HIS MONEY. HE FOLLOWS THE CREATURE'S TRAIL FOR YEARS.

VICTOR HUNTS THE CREATURE TO THE NORTH POLE. HE BECOMES SO TIRED AND SICK THAT HE COLLAPSES.

CAPTAIN ROBERT WALTON IS LEADING AN EXPEDITION TO THE NORTH POLE. HE TAKES CARE OF VICTOR.

WHEN VICTOR GAINS ENOUGH STRENGTH, HE TELLS THE CAPTAIN HIS STORY.

A FEW DAYS LATER, WALTON STOPS BY TO VISIT VICTOR ...

... AND SEES THE CREATURE. WALTON IS TERRIFIED! HE EXPECTS THE CREATURE TO ATTACK HIM, BUT TO HIS SURPRISE, THE CREATURE JUST SPEAKS.

He is dead. I came to ask him to forgive me, but I am too late. I have lost someone I love. Now I know the pain I have caused him.

I now know what it is like to be human. My creator—Victor Frankenstein— is gone.